C000126930

Testing and assessment in the National Curriculum

Pupils between the ages of 7 and 11 (Years 3–6) cover Key Stage 2 of the National Curriculum. In May of their final year of Key Stage 2 (Year 6) all pupils take written National Tests (commonly known as SATs) in the three most important subjects: English, Mathematics and Science. Your child may already have taken some National Tests at the end of Key Stage 1 (Year 2). These will have been in number, shape and space, reading, writing, handwriting and spelling.

At the end of Key Stage 1, your child will have been awarded a National Curriculum level for each subject tested. When your child eventually takes the Key Stage 2 tests, he or she again will be awarded a level. On average, pupils are expected to advance one level for every two years they are at school. The target for pupils at the end of Key Stage 1 is Level 2. By the end of Key Stage 2, four years later, the target is Level 4. The table below will show you how your child should progress.

		7 years	11 years
■ Exceptional performance	Level 6		■
	Level 5		▦
▦ Exceeded targets for age group	Level 4	▦	▢
▢ Achieved targets for age group	Level 3	▦	▢
	Level 2	▦	▢
▢ Working towards targets for age group	Level 1	▢	▢

Assessing your child's progress throughout Key Stage 2 of the National Curriculum

The aim of the Letts Assessment books is to help you monitor your child's progress in English, Mathematics and Science throughout Key Stage 2. There are four books for each subject – one for each year, starting with 7–8 year olds. The questions in the books become progressively harder with each year, so that for 10–11 year olds, the questions will be at a level similar to the Key Stage 2 National Tests.

After completing a book, your child will have a score which you will be able to interpret using the progress indicator provided. This will give you a guide to the level at which your child is working.

ASSESSING YOUR CHILD'S PROGRESS

Using this book to assess your child's progress in Science

This book is for 8–9 year olds (Year 4). It contains four basic features:

Questions:	31 questions, arranged in order of difficulty as follows:
	9 at Level 2 (pages 1–9)
	9 at Level 3 (pages 10–20)
	4 at Level 3/4 (pages 21–25)
	9 at Level 4 (pages 26–37)
Answers:	showing acceptable responses and marks
Note to Parent:	giving advice on what your child should be doing and how to help
Progress Chart:	showing you how to interpret your child's marks to arrive at a level

- Your child should not attempt to do all the questions in the book in one go. Try setting ten questions at a time. If your child does not understand a question, you might want to explain it. Although the questions in this book are not meant to constitute a formal test, you should encourage your child to answer as many as possible without help. Read the questions to your child if you think it will help.

- When your child has completed the questions, turn to the Answer section at the back of the book. Using the recommended answers, award your child the appropriate mark or marks for each question. In the margin of each question page, there are small boxes. These are divided in half with the marks available for that question at the bottom, and a blank at the top for you to fill in your child's score.

- Collate your child's marks on the grid on page 46. Then add them up. Once you have the total, turn to page 38 at the front of the Answer section and look at the Progress Chart to determine your child's level.

- Work through the answers with your child, using the Note to Parent to help give advice, correct mistakes and explain problems.

Equipment your child will need for this book

All your child needs are a pen or pencil for writing, and a pencil for drawing. Your child may also like to have a rubber for changing answers. Where lines have to be drawn, they can be drawn either with a ruler or freehand, whichever your child feels most comfortable with.

1 Snakes are cold-blooded and need to live in a warm climate.

Polar bears have thick fur to keep them warm.

Seals feed on fish.

Penguins swim in cold water and catch fish.

What is wrong with these pictures?

4

Q1

✏ a ....

....

✏ b ....

....

✏ c ....

....

✏ d ....

....

Letts

2

Where does the light come from in each of these pictures?

a

....

....

b

....

....

c

....

....

d

....

....

3 Timothy found some things in his toy cupboard.

steel toy car

glass marble

teddy bear

balloon

Here are some descriptions for each of the things Timothy found. Tick ✓ the boxes to match each thing with its description. The first one has been done for you.

	steel toy car	balloon	glass marble	teddy bear
is see-through	☐	☐	✓	☐
is smooth and can stretch	☐	☐	☐	☐
is soft to touch	☐	☐	☐	☐
is attracted by a magnet	☐	☐	☐	☐

3

Q3

4 Mr Green wants to start growing some vegetables in his greenhouse.

a (Circle) **three** things that the plants will need to grow.

water

garden spade

Sun

potting compost

Moon

sand

b Why do plants grow better in the greenhouse than in the garden?

....

c Why do plants grow better in the greenhouse than in the shed?

....

5   Mandy left her chocolate bar in the sun. The pictures show the chocolate before and after it was left.

before   after

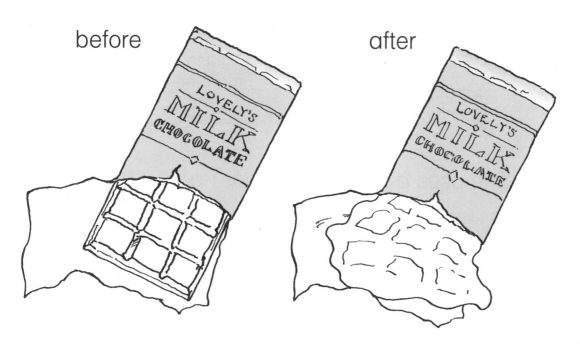

a   <u>Underline</u> the word which describes the chocolate bar before it was left.

1

Q5a

gas   **liquid**   **solid**

b   Choose words from the list to complete the sentences.

2

Q5b

boiled   **cooker**   **fridge**   **melted**

Mandy's chocolate has ....

She can turn it hard again by putting it in a

.... to make it cold.

5

6 Sarah has dropped her dad's box of odds and ends all over the garage floor.

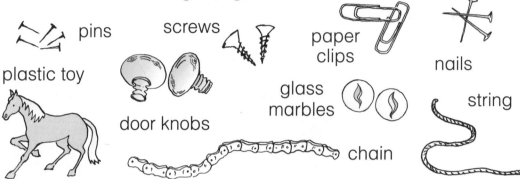

pins   screws   paper clips   nails

plastic toy   door knobs   glass marbles   string   chain

She uses a magnet to clear up.

a

Write the name of each object in the table.

magnet will pick up	magnet will not pick up

4

Q6a

Class 6 like recycling aluminium cans. They want to make sure there are no steel cans in their collection.

b

How can they check for steel cans?

1

Q6b

....

....

7 Jane collected four objects from around her house and then filled in a chart to show the materials the objects were made from. Jane's friend Susan had to match the number to the object. Here is the chart:

object	wood	wax	plastic	metal	paper
1					✓
2		✓			
3	✓				
4			✓	✓	

Draw lines to link the object to the number.

number	object
1	 pen
2	book
3	candle
4	 ruler

4

Q7

7

Letts

8   Look at these circuits.

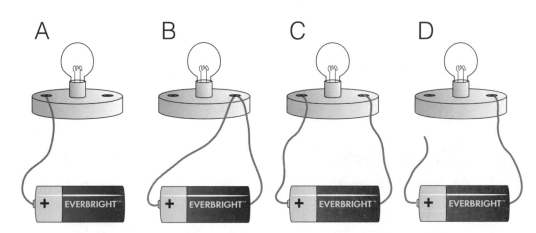

A   B   C   D

a   Which bulb will light?

bulb ....

Something has been added to each circuit.

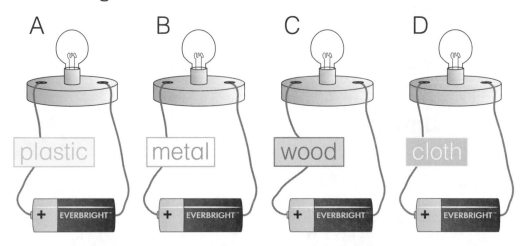

A   B   C   D

plastic   metal   wood   cloth

b   Which one will light now? Fill in the blanks in
the sentence.

Bulb .... will light now because ....

conducts electricity and the others do not.

9 Sarah and Thomas study the animals that live in a pile of leaves in their garden. This is what they find:

worms   spiders   centipedes

a How many animals did they find?

1

Q9a

Sarah and Thomas write their findings in a table.

b Finish the table.

3

Q9b

	number found
centipede	4

c Write down **two** differences between centipedes and spiders.

2

Q9c

1 ....

2 ....

9

10 The picture shows the food in Jennifer's lunch box.

biscuit   milk   crisps

peanut butter sandwiches

a

| 1 |
| Q10a |

Circle the food that helps to keep Jennifer's teeth strong.

b

| 1 |
| Q10b |

What else must Jennifer do to help keep her teeth strong?

Jennifer's mum wants her to have another piece of food to help keep her healthy.

c

| 1 |
| Q10c |

Tick ✓ the box which would be the best food to add.

apple   ☐

lemonade   ☐

sweets   ☐

11 Kate has made
some ice cubes
in the freezer.

John has
made a model
from wet clay.

Laura baked a
small loaf of bread
in the oven.

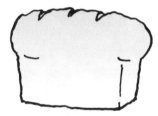

What would happen to each thing if it was left in the sun for a day?

3

Q11

a The ice cubes ....

b The clay model ....

c The bread ....

12   Look at this picture of a pen.

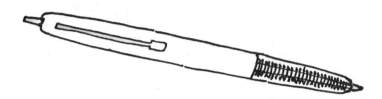

a

When you press the top to use the pen, what happens to the spring?

1
Q12a

....

....

Look at these kitchen scales.

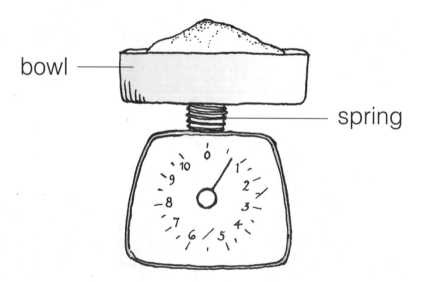

bowl

spring

b

When you put some flour into the bowl, what happens to the spring?

1
Q12b

....

....

c

What happens to the spring when you take the weight off the scales?

1

Q12c

....

....

Look at this open gate.

d

Why does the gate close after you let it go?

1

Q12d

....

....

13

5

Q13

What material does the builder use for each part of the house? Choose from the list below.

wood   copper   glass   plastic   bricks

a outside walls ....

b water pipes ....

c stairs ....

d windows ....

e roof supports ....

14   Look at the pictures.

a | Tick ✓ **one** box to show what the cat and the toy mouse can both do. |

grow ☐

move ☐

reproduce ☐

1

Q14a

b | The cat is a living thing. Tick ✓ **two** boxes to show what the cat must do to stay alive. |

breathe ☐

eat food ☐

stay in sunlight ☐

swim ☐

2

Q14b

15

15 Nigel and Pam are playing a guessing game. Nigel has put something in the box and Pam has to guess if it is a living thing or not.

1

Q15

Tick ✓ the best question for Pam to ask.

Can it move? ☐

Does it need to be kept warm? ☐

Can it reproduce itself? ☐

Does it need water? ☐

Is it light or heavy? ☐

16 If you add things to water some will mix with the water and **dissolve**.

a
| Does salt dissolve in water? |

1
Q16a

....

b
| Does sand dissolve in water? |

1
Q16b

....

c
| Write the name of each thing in the correct container of water. One has been done for you. |

5
Q16c

| salt | sand | chalk | sugar |
| oil | sawdust | 5p coin | grass |

sand

dissolves   does not dissolve

Letts

17 Jo did an experiment on growing plants.

The words tell you what Jo did to each plant.

The pictures show how the plants looked after two weeks.

a

> Draw a line to join each set of words to the correct picture.

Jo left the plants in a dark cupboard.

Jo forgot to water the plants.

Jo left the plants in bright sunshine near a window.

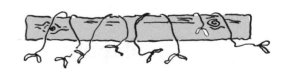

Jo also placed one set of plants in a freezer and left them for two weeks.

b Tick ✓ the sentence that best describes how the plants looked when Jo took them out of the freezer.

The plants looked the same. ☐

The plants had grown taller. ☐

The plants had all died. ☐

1

Q17b

c Write down **two** things a plant needs for it to grow.

2

Q17c

1 ....

2 ....

18 At school Jackie listened to sounds made by different things. The pictures show the things that made the sounds.

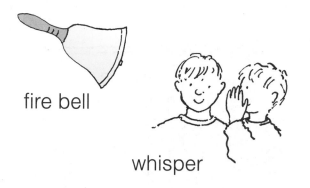

fire bell

whisper

clapping

whistle

a

Finish writing a list of the sounds in order of how loud they were.

loudest _____ *fire bell* _____

_____

_____

quietest _____

Daniel went outside while the rest of the class stayed in the classroom and made the sounds again.

3

Q18a

b

Put a ⟨circle⟩ around the best description of how Daniel heard the sounds.

The sounds were:

louder   **quieter**   **the same**

1

Q18b

19 Mr Smith and Mr Jones used seeds from the same packet to grow cabbages in their gardens. Mr Smith's cabbages grew very well, but Mr Jones' cabbages did not grow well at all.

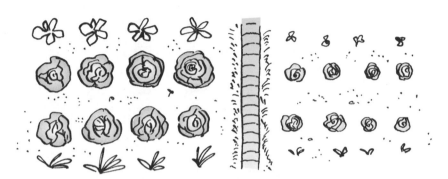

a

> Give **three** reasons why Mr Smith's cabbages grew better than Mr Jones' cabbages.

1 ....

2 ....

3 ....

Cabbage white butterflies lay their eggs on cabbage leaves. The eggs turn into caterpillars. Birds eat the caterpillars.

b

> Put the words **bird**, **caterpillar** and **leaf** in the correct boxes in this food chain.

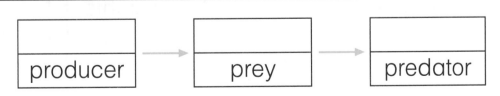

| producer | → | prey | → | predator |

3
Q19a

3
Q19b

20 Concrete is made by mixing together sand, cement and water. It sets hard.

sand

cement

water

a

Which of these materials are natural? Put a

sand ☐

cement ☐

water ☐

2

Q20a

Jo makes different concrete bars and tests them like this to see how strong they are.

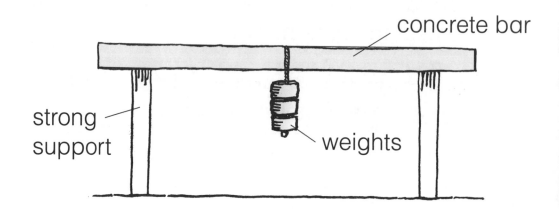

concrete bar

strong
support

weights

Here are the results:

	amount of sand	amount of cement	weight needed to break the bar
bar 1	4 parts	1 part	400 grams
bar 2	3 parts	1 part	600 grams
bar 3	2 parts	1 part	450 grams
bar 4	1 part	1 part	300 grams

b Which bar is strongest?

....

c Write down **two** things Jo must do to make it a **fair test**.

1 ....

2 ....

1

Q20b

2

Q20c

21 Look at these pictures.

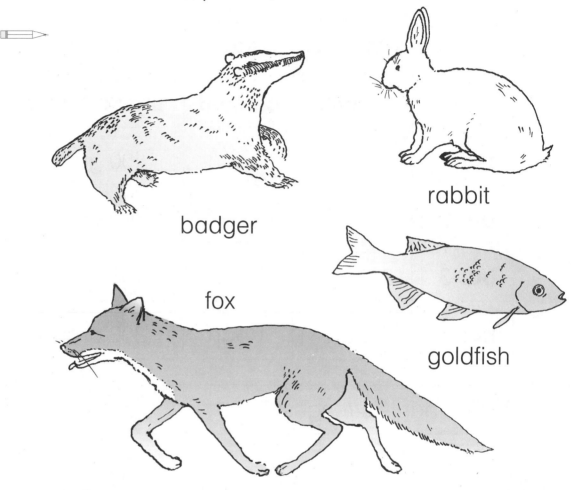

badger

rabbit

fox

goldfish

a Circle the animal that lives in water.

1

Q21a

b Name **one** part of the animal that helps it to swim.

1

Q21b

....

c Which part of the animal allows it to breathe?

1

Q21c

....

22 John watched his dad making some chocolate cakes. The pictures show what was on the kitchen table.

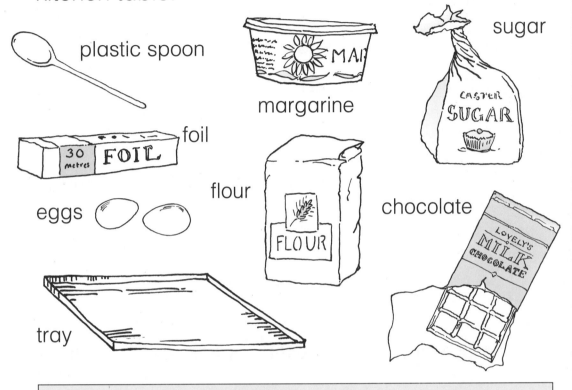

From the pictures choose:

a Two things made from metal.

.... and ....

b Two things which are natural.

.... and ....

c Two things which will burn.

.... and ....

d Two things which will melt when warmed.

.... and ....

8

Q22

23 Simon found four shells on the beach. He used a key to find out what they were.

Here is the key:

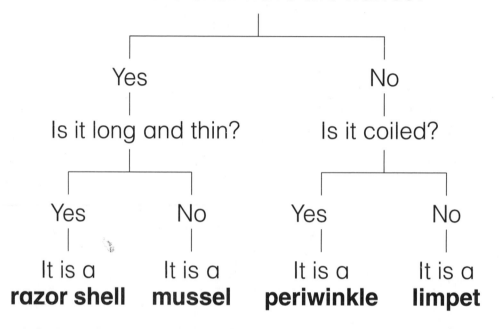

Does the shell have two halves?

Yes　　　　　　　　　　No

Is it long and thin?　　　Is it coiled?

Yes　　　　No　　　　Yes　　　　No

It is a　　　It is a　　　It is a　　　It is a
razor shell　**mussel**　**periwinkle**　**limpet**

Use the key to fill in the names of the shells Simon found underneath the pictures.

a _____　b _____

c _____　d _____

4

Q23

24   The picture shows a large soft ball resting on the ground.

The arrow shows the force on the ball.

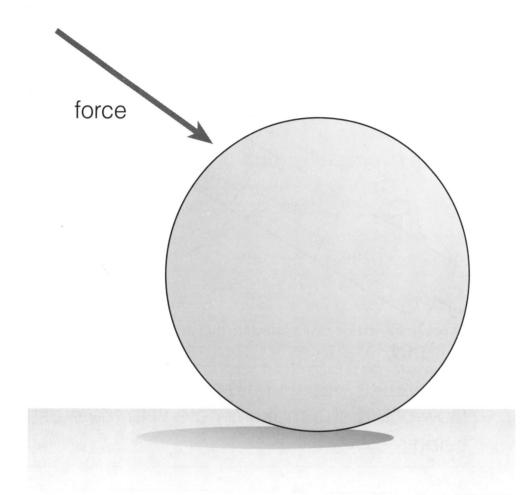

force

What **two** different things could the force do to the ball?

1 ....

2 ....

3

Q24

25 Donna made her own musical instrument.

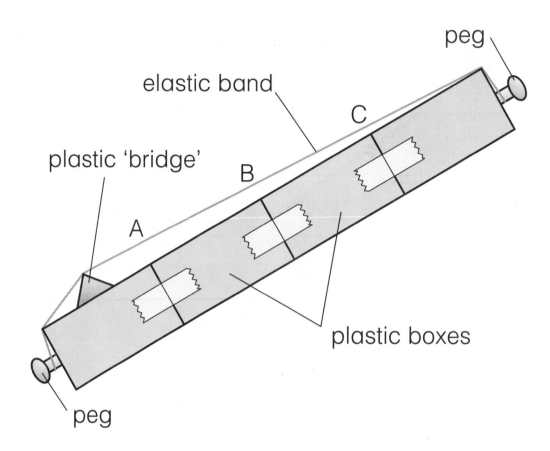

peg

elastic band

C

plastic 'bridge'

B

A

plastic boxes

peg

a

1

Q25a

> How could she make a note with the elastic band?

....

If Donna pressed down with the elastic band, she could change the note she made.

b

1

Q25b

> Where should she press to make the highest note – at **A**, **B** or **C**?

....

c Write down another way she could make the note higher or lower.

....

....

d If she looked closely at the elastic band as it made a note, what would she notice?

....

....

e Write down the name of an instrument that works like Donna's.

....

26   This circuit is switched off.

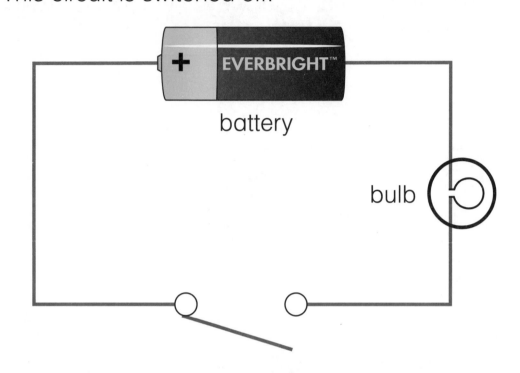

a

Draw in the switch so that the bulb will light.

1

Q26a

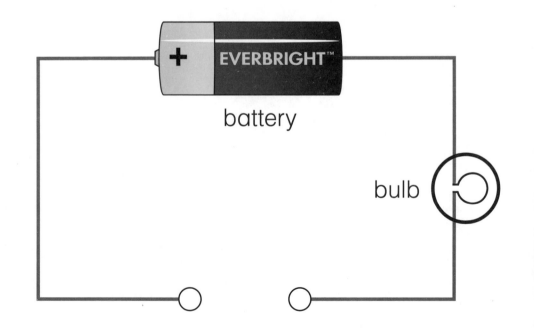

Letts

b

In these circuits, which bulb will light?

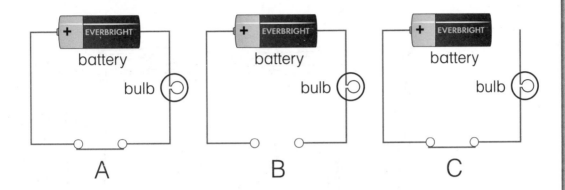

A   B   C

Bulb .... will light.

Bulb .... will not light because ....

....

Bulb .... will not light because ....

....

This is the symbol for an electric motor:

c

Draw a diagram with a switch that would make an electric motor work in the box below.

27 John's aunt is pushing her car to get it into the garage.

4

Q27

Fill in the gaps in the sentences below using any of the words from the list.

friction   grip   move   pull   push

 The car will only _____ if a force is

acting on it. When John's aunt starts to _____,

the car moves. John's aunt has got trainers on.

These help her to _____ the drive. The

force which stops her slipping on the drive is

called _____ .

28 Ben used a tea strainer to separate tea leaves from tea.

tea leaves   strainer

tea

a Explain why the tea leaves did not go through the holes in the tea strainer.

1

Q28a

....

b <u>Underline</u> the word which best describes the kind of separation Ben used.

1

Q28b

chromatography   **condensation**

distillation   **filtration**

c Tick ✓ **one** box to show which two things could be separated in the same way.

1

Q28c

oil and water ☐

sand and water ☐

salt and water ☐

29 Sacha and Duncan are testing how far a marble rolls on different surfaces. They let the marble go from a slope.

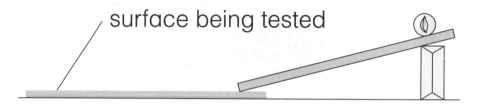

surface being tested

These are the surfaces they test:

carpet   **wood**   **sand**

a

On which surface will the marble travel furthest?

b

Give the reason why you chose this one.

c

What should they use to measure how far the marble rolls?

d

Write down **one** thing they should do to make sure the test is **fair**.

Letts

Here are Sacha and Duncan's results:

surface	how far the marble rolls
carpet	15 cm
wood	35 cm
sand	10 cm

e Draw their results as a bar chart on the grid below.

3

Q29e

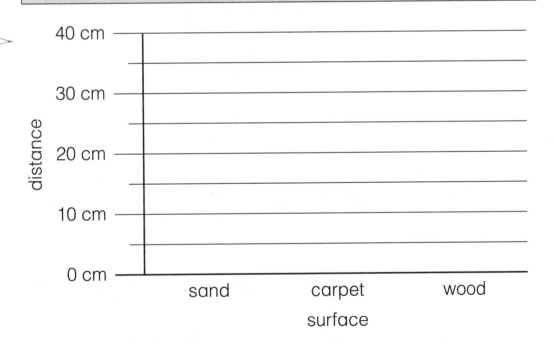

f What type of surface allows the marble to travel furthest?

1

Q29f

....

30 These pictures are all drawings of the parts of a buttercup flower.

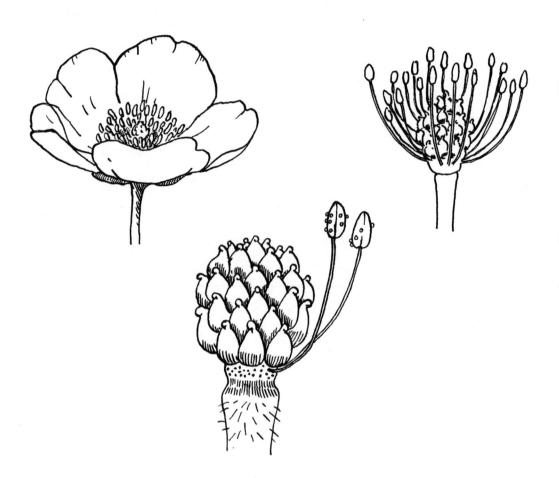

Finish the sentences by choosing words from the list.

anthers petals sepals stamens stigmas

➡ If you pull off the .... and the .... you can see the parts inside the flower. The part in the centre is called the pistil. The parts of the pistil are called ....

31 On a sunny day in the summer Roy pushed a stick into the ground.

The picture shows the shadow at 9 o'clock in the morning.

9 o'clock in the morning

Draw in the shadows at these other times during the day.

4

Q31

a

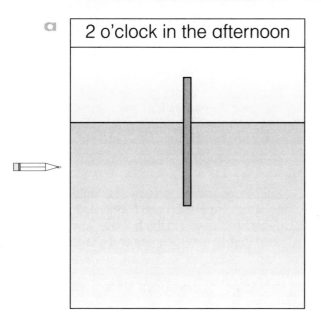

2 o'clock in the afternoon

b

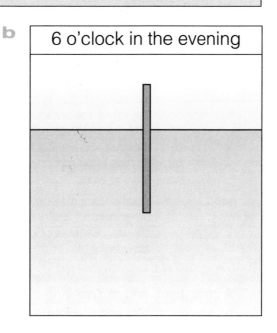

6 o'clock in the evening

MARKING YOUR CHILD'S QUESTIONS

- When marking your child's questions, remember that the answers given here are the answers the question-setter expects. You must look at your child's answers and judge whether they deserve credit.

- At this age, your child's spelling may show a number of errors. Do not mark any answer wrong because the words are misspelt. Read the word aloud and, if it sounds correct, award the mark. For example, 'ekwul' would be acceptable for 'equal'.

- When you go through the questions with your child, try to be positive. Look for good things that have been done in addition to showing where errors have been made.

- Enter your child's marks on the grid on page 46, and then refer to the table below to determine your child's level.

Progress Chart

Total marks scored	Progress made	Suggested action
25 or below	Your child has acquired some of the knowledge, skills and understanding associated with Level 2 work.	Identify areas of weakness from Levels 2 and 3 of the test. Encourage your child to study living things, investigate the properties of everyday materials and construct simple circuits.
26–50	Your child is confident in working with several scientific concepts at Level 2 and is beginning to show achievement at Level 3.	Discuss with your child the changes that take place: to living things as they grow; and to non-living things with a change of temperature.
51–75	Your child has mastered Level 2 work and is showing skills associated with scientific understanding at Level 3.	Encourage your child to link cause and effect by asking questions such as, 'Why does that ball move?' Ask your child to identify the parts of flowers.
75–100	Your child is displaying the majority of the knowledge, skills and understanding required at Level 3 and is starting to grasp Level 4 ideas.	Play games that require your child to know the scientific names for body organs and parts of flowers. Encourage a study of the Sun and planets. Allow your child to use the kitchen to study dissolving and filtering.
101 and above	Your child is making rapid progress and is already showing aspects of Level 4 achievement.	Encourage the correct use of scientific terms such as evaporation and condensation to describe changes in the home. Allow your child to play with magnets and shadows.

- A child at the end of Year 4 (8–9 year olds) should be, of the above statements, between the third and the fourth statements.

1 a It is too cold for the snake   *1 mark*
   b It is too hot for the polar bear.   *1 mark*
   c There is nowhere for the seal to swim or catch fish.   *1 mark*
   d It is too hot *or* there is nowhere for the penguin to swim or catch fish. *1 mark*

> **Note to Parent**
>
> This question assesses whether or not your child recognises that animals are suited to particular environments. You can encourage your child to make progress by asking questions, such as 'How is this animal or plant suited to where it lives?'

                                                                               Total 4 marks

2 a the Sun   *1 mark*
   b headlights   *1 mark*
   c candles   *1 mark*
   d torch   *1 mark*
                                                                               Total 4 marks

3 is smooth and can stretch – balloon   *1 mark*
   is soft to touch – teddy bear   *1 mark*
   is attracted by a magnet – steel toy car   *1 mark*

> **Note to Parent**
>
> This question assesses whether or not your child can use everyday properties to compare different materials. Children can make progress at home by being encouraged to point out similarities and differences when comparing two objects.

                                                                               Total 3 marks

4 a potting compost, water, Sun   *1 mark each*
   b it is warmer *or*
      they are sheltered from the cold or wind   *1 mark*
   c there is more light in the greenhouse *or*
      it is dark in the shed   *1 mark*

> **Note to Parent**
>
> At this level children should realise that plant growth depends on light, water and temperature. Plants do not need food to grow – they make their own food. Potting compost anchors the roots and stores water, while the Sun provides heat and light. An answer to part **c** that the greenhouse is made of glass is not sufficient to gain the mark.

                                                                               Total 5 marks

5 a solid   *1 mark*
   b melted   fridge   *2 marks*

> **Note to Parent**
>
> This question tests an understanding of how materials are changed by heating and cooling. As your child progresses, he or she will learn to distinguish between reversible and non-reversible changes.

                                                                               Total 3 marks

6 a will pick up: screws, chain, nails, pins, paper clips
Award two marks for four or more correct; one mark for two or three correct   *2 marks*
will not pick up: string, plastic toy, door knob, marbles
Award two marks for three or more correct; one mark for two correct   *2 marks*
   b they can check the cans with a magnet. Steel cans will be attracted to the magnet   *1 mark*

Note to Parent

This question is testing whether your child knows that there are forces of attraction between magnets and magnetic materials. Some children think that magnets pick up all metals. The common magnetic materials that your child will come across are iron, steel and nickel (found in coins). Other metals, such as aluminium, are not attracted to magnets.

Total 5 marks

7 1 is the book   *1 mark*
   2 is the candle   *1 mark*
   3 is the ruler   *1 mark*
   4 is the pen   *1 mark*
Total 4 marks

8 a C   *1 mark*
   b B   metal   *1 mark each*

Note to Parent

Children can make progress at home by experimenting with lamps, motors, batteries and wire. Some kits are very expensive, but the contents can be bought as individual items very cheaply.

Total 3 marks

9 a 13   *1 mark*

Note to Parent

This question is testing whether your child understands that living things are either plants or animals. There is often confusion at this age about animals, birds and insects. In fact none of the animals shown are insects.

   b Left hand column headed 'animal'   *1 mark*
   The rows should read (in either order)
   worms   6   *1 mark*
   spiders   3   *1 mark*
   c they have different numbers of legs   *1 mark*
   centipedes have long *or* thin bodies *or* lots of segments   *1 mark*
   Award the mark for any one answer

Total 6 marks

10 a milk   *1 mark*
   b she must clean or brush her teeth   *1 mark*
   c apple   *1 mark*

Note to Parent

This question is testing your child's understanding of a healthy diet and the importance of dental care.

Total 3 marks

11 a will melt *or* change to water   *1 mark*
    b will dry *or* harden   *1 mark*
    c will go dry   *1 mark*

Note to Parent

Your child should be beginning to distinguish between reversible and non-reversible changes.

Total 3 marks

12 a the spring becomes smaller/shorter/squashed   *1 mark*
    b the spring becomes smaller/flatter/squashed   *1 mark*
    c the spring becomes bigger/taller/unsquashed   *1 mark*
    d the spring pulls it shut   *1 mark*

Total 4 marks

13 a bricks   *1 mark*
    b copper *or* plastic   *1 mark*
    c wood   *1 mark*
    d glass   *1 mark*
    e wood   *1 mark*

Note to Parent

Encourage your child to explain why some everyday materials are particularly suitable for specific purposes. This will help your child to make progress.

Total 5 marks

14 a move   *1 mark*
    b breathe and eat food   *1 mark each*

Note to Parent

There are a number of processes that all living things go through. Some of these, such as movement, are also common in some non-living things.

Total 3 marks

15 Can it reproduce itself?   *1 mark*

Note to Parent

This question assesses if your child knows that the essential difference between living and non-living things is whether or not they grow and reproduce themselves.

Total 1 mark

16 a yes   *1 mark*
    b no   *1 mark*
    c dissolves: salt, sugar   *1 mark each*
       does not dissolve: chalk, oil, sawdust, 5p coin, grass
       Award three marks for all five correct; two marks for four; one mark for three   *3 marks*

Note to Parent

Children can learn about dissolving by experimenting with small amounts of everyday substances at home. No special equipment is needed; just a spoon, a cup and some water.

Total 7 marks

17 a Lines from:

	to:	
left in a dark cupboard	middle picture	*1 mark*
Jo forgot to water the plants	bottom picture	*1 mark*
Jo left the plants in bright sunshine	top picture	*1 mark*

If more than one line is drawn from a description do not award marks

  b The plants had all died   *1 mark*

  c Any two from:
   water, light, warmth   *2 marks*

Note to Parent

Your child will probably be confident with the answer of water but you might need to explain that other things are needed for healthy growth in plants.

Total 6 marks

18 a whistle, clapping, whisper   *3 marks*

   If the order is not correct, award a mark if whistle is before clapping; a mark if clapping is before whisper; and a mark if whistle is before whisper.

  b quieter   *1 mark*

Note to Parent

Your child should by now be starting to explain physical effects, such as sounds being quieter or louder.

Total 4 marks

19 a Any three from:
   Mr Smith's cabbages have more light, more water, better soil or more nutrients
   Mr Jones' cabbages suffer from pests or disease   *1 mark each*

  b producer – leaf   *1 mark*
   prey – caterpillar   *1 mark*
   predator – bird   *1 mark*

Total 6 marks

20 a sand   *1 mark*
   water   *1 mark*

  b bar 2   *1 mark*

  c Any two of:
   same sized bar
   same distance between the supports
   bar dried for same length of time   *2 marks*

Note to Parent

In part **c** your child may give two things that both relate to size, for example same length, width and depth. Award both marks in this case. The idea of fair testing is important.

Total 5 marks

21 a goldfish   *1 mark*
     b fins *or* tail   *1 mark*
     c gills   *1 mark*
                      Total 3 marks

22 a tray and foil   *2 marks*
     b Any two of: flour, eggs, sugar   *2 marks*
     c Any two of: plastic spoon, flour, eggs, sugar, chocolate, margarine   *2 marks*
     d Any two of: margarine, chocolate, plastic spoon   *2 marks*

Note to Parent

As children progress from level 3 to level 4, they increase their knowledge about the properties of different materials and are able to explain why these properties make the materials suitable to their use.

                      Total 8 marks

23 a periwinkle   *1 mark*
     b razor shell   *1 mark*
     c mussel   *1 mark*
     d limpet   *1 mark*

Note to Parent

Your child can make progress by constructing and using keys to separate and identify everyday household objects.

                      Total 4 marks

24 1 make the ball move   *1 mark*
        it will move to the right   *1 mark*
     2 squash it *or* change its shape   *1 mark*

Note to Parent

Encourage your child to link forces with their effects, such as a change in shape, speed or direction of movement.

                      Total 3 marks

25 a she could pluck it, *or* flick it, *or* scrape it, *or* 'ping' it (**not** pull it back)   *1 mark*
     b A   *1 mark*
     c she could move the bridge *or* tighten the elastic band   *1 mark*
     d the elastic band would move up and down *or* from side to side   *1 mark*
     e For example: violin, guitar, cello   *1 mark*

Note to Parent

The question is testing your child's developing ideas of how sounds are caused and how the pitch can be changed. Children learn a great deal of science through play and these valuable experiences should be encouraged.

                      Total 5 marks

26 a a line should be drawn between the two small circles *1 mark*
    b A *1 mark*
       B will not light because the circuit is not complete *or* it is switched off *1 mark*
       C will not light because a wire is missing *or* the circuit is not complete *1 mark*
    c

1 mark

Note to Parent

The components in the circuit in part **c** can be drawn in any order. The switch can be drawn open (off) or closed (on).

Total 5 marks

27 move *1 mark*
    push *1 mark*
    grip *1 mark*
    friction *1 mark*

Note to Parent

If John's aunt was wearing smooth soled shoes and if the drive was very smooth, it is unlikely that she would be able to move the car, however strong she was. The term friction is important for children to know. Friction is the force that stops things from slipping or sliding. Look, for example, around the home for surfaces which are designed to increase or decrease friction.

Total 4 marks

28 a the leaves are too big *1 mark*
    b filtration *1 mark*
    c sand and water *1 mark*

Note to Parent

At Level 4, children are beginning to learn how different methods can be used to separate mixtures.

Total 3 marks

29 a wood *1 mark*
    b it is smooth *or* the others are rough *1 mark*
    c a ruler *1 mark*
    d let go of the marble from the same place *1 mark*

e
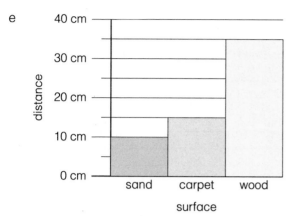

Award one mark for each bar correctly completed 3 marks

f   a smooth one 1 mark

Note to Parent

In part **c** your child might answer 'use the marble', but a fair test can be done using different marbles, provided they are the same size and weight. For part **f** wood is not a correct answer since the question is about the type of surface.

Total 8 marks

30 sepals and petals (in either order) *1 mark each*
stigmas *1 mark*

Note to Parent

This question assesses whether or not your child can identify the parts of different flowers. It is important that children have experience of a wide range of flowers. All flowers have the parts which children need to know about, but the size, shape and number of each part varies from flower to flower. Daffodils, for example, only have one stigma, but a crocus, like the buttercup, has more than one.

Total 3 marks

31 a   The shadow should be just to the left of centre *1 mark*
        and shorter than the morning shadow *1 mark*
    b   The shadow should be well to the left of centre *1 mark*
        and longer than the morning shadow *1 mark*

Note to Parent

To answer this question, your child needs to know how the apparent position of the Sun changes during the day.

Total 4 marks

MARKING GRID

Question	Marks available	Marks scored
1	4	
2	4	
3	3	
4	5	
5	3	
6	5	
7	4	
8	3	
9	6	
Total	37	

Question	Marks available	Marks scored
10	3	
11	3	
12	4	
13	5	
14	3	
15	1	
16	7	
17	6	
18	4	
Total	36	

Question	Marks available	Marks scored
19	6	
20	5	
21	3	
22	8	
Total	22	

Question	Marks available	Marks scored
23	4	
24	3	
25	5	
26	5	
27	4	
28	3	
29	8	
30	3	
31	4	
Total	39	